Spelling Module

Chris Burgess

•

Designed and illustrated by Anne Isseyegh

Schofield & Sims Ltd

To the Reader

The books in the ENGLISH SKILLS series are designed to provide pupils with a broad range of practice material in the basic skills of language. The series can be used as a resource for pupils who need reinforcement in particular areas of weakness. The material is also useful as immediate follow-up exercises to direct teaching of the skills.

Although the reading difficulty of the exercises has been kept at a level suitable for pupils of 9+, the content is sufficiently mature for Secondary students who require practice in the skills covered.

English Skills, Study Reading and Working with Information

The modules in this series are complementary to the modules in STUDY READING and the books in WORKING WITH INFORMATION. Together, the three series give comprehensive coverage of the skills of language communication.

ENGLISH SKILLS deals mainly with the conventions of language usage, including as it does modules on *Punctuation, Written Communication, Spelling* and *Vocabulary.* Additionally, there are titles on *Creative Writing* and *Reference Skills.*

STUDY READING is a reading development programme ranging in reading ages from 6.0 to 12.5, in which the emphasis is on the extracting of information from printed materials.

WORKING WITH INFORMATION provides practice in reference and study skills, and the writing of projects.

0 7217 0605 3

First printed 1986
Reprinted 1986
Reprinted 1988
Reprinted 1991

Typesetting by Armitage Typo/Graphics Ltd., Huddersfield
Printed in England by Garnett Dickinson Print Ltd., Rotherham and London.

Contents

Short Vowel Sounds

In the alphabet, letters **a**, **e**, **i**, **o** and **u** are vowels.

The other letters are consonants.

Sometimes the letters **w** and **y** are used as vowels.

The vowels **a**, **e**, **i**, **o** and **u** can be used to spell short sounds:

short **a** sound in **plan**
short **e** sound in **left**
short **i** sound in **sink**
short **o** sound in **shot**
short **u** sound in **duck**

A Fill the blanks with the letters that spell words with one short vowel sound. Write the whole word.

Question: fl_____ ea, at
Answer: flat

1 g_____ oe, um
2 sh_____ ut, oe
3 p_____ ay, in
4 m_____ ap, ae
5 d____k ei, ec
6 s_____ ie, ix
7 sh_____ oe, op
8 d____k oe, oc
9 m_____ ie, ix
10 f_____ oe, ox
11 dr_____ aw, op
12 sl_____ ae, ap
13 l____k oo, oc
14 sp_____ out, ot
15 l____p ea, um
16 n____t ex, ea
17 m_____s es, ee
18 b____k ea, ac
19 kn____k oo, oc
20 m____t us, oa

Short *e* in *mess*

Short **a** Sound

Many words have a short **a** sound before one or more final consonants. It is spelled **a** as in **bat**.

B Fill the blanks with the letters that spell a word with a short **a** sound. Write the whole word.

Question: s_____d an, ae
Answer: sand

1 th_____ at, ae
2 l_____ ea, ap
3 t_____ ea, ap
4 n_____ ap, ail
5 r_____ ai, an
6 th____k an, ea
7 s_____ ad, aid
8 p_____ lane, an
9 b_____g an, ea
10 h_____ at, ate
11 gr_____ ae, ab
12 b_____ ad, ae
13 m____ch at, ea
14 s_____ ae, at
15 str_____ aw, ap
16 tr_____ ap, ain

C Rearrange the letters to make words with a short **a** sound.

1 sha   2 nam   3 calk   4 lashl
5 kabln   6 kabn   7 casnk   8 apkc

Sounds the Same – 1

There are some words that sound alike, but have different meanings.
They are usually spelled differently—
son and **sun** sound alike.

A Fill the blanks in the sentences with the words in brackets. Write the whole sentences. If you are in doubt, look up the meanings of the words in a dictionary.

Question: _____ the time we get to the shops, it will be too late to _____ anything.
(buy, by)
Answer: By the time we get to the shops, it will be too late to buy anything.

1 In less than an _____, it will be _____ turn to guard the prisoners. (our, hour)

2 It's _____ late to get _____ more tickets for the Cup Final. (two, too)

3 Very soon it will be _____ dark _____ play cricket. (to, too)

4 Through the _____ trees of the forest we saw the grizzly _____ approaching. (bear, bare)

5 If you stand quietly _____, you will _____ the waves breaking on the beach. (hear, here)

6 _____ many cooks in one kitchen always lead _____ trouble. (too, to)

7 It is more than a _____ since the accident, but I still feel very _____. (weak, week)

8 Trevor is not able to _____ with his _____ hand. (right, write)

Long **a** Sound

A vowel is long when it makes the sound of its name: **baby**.
The long **a** sound is spelled with one letter in **baby**.
When a long **a** sound comes at the end of a word, it is spelled **ay**: **play**.

B Make words with a long a sound by adding a or ay. Write the whole word.

Question: s____
Answer: say

1 m____
2 ____ge
3 d____
4 del____
5 rel____
6 l____dy
7 p____per
8 p____
9 st____ble
10 str____

11 ____ble
12 l____ter
13 r____dio
14 cl____
15 l____
16 ____pe
17 holid____
18 st____
19 avi____tion
20 sh____dy.

C Here is a sentence containing four long a sounds: "The lady said she would pay for the wallpaper later."

1 Write a sentence containing four long **a** sounds. Underline the letters that spell the long **a** sounds. Do not use the words used in the example.

2 Write a sentence containing four short **a** sounds. Underline the letters that spell the short **a** sounds.

Often Misspelled – 1

Some words are often misspelled. When you need to write a word and you are not sure how to spell it, check in a dictionary.

A Read the meaning of each word. Then complete the spelling of the word. Each star stands for one letter. Write the whole word.

> Question: In company   t*g*th*r
> Answer: together

1 Land with water all round it   i*land
2 Adult female person   w*m*n
3 Fast   q**ck
4 To answer without knowledge   g**ss
5 The same in number or size, etc.   eq**l
6 Messenger from God   ang**
7 A machine that gives power to do work
                                         en*in*
8 Knowledge got by study and testing
                                         s*i*nce

"Success! Now I know it works!"

Long **e** Sound

The long **e** sound at the beginning of a word is usually spelled **ea**: **eat**
The long **e** sound in the middle of a word is usually spelled **ee** or **ea**: **feet peach**
The long **e** sound at the end of a word is usually spelled **ee**: **free**

B Make words with a long **e** sound by adding **ea** or **ee**.

> Question: m____l
> Answer: meal

1 s____d   11 pl____
2 l____d   12 tr____t
3 tr____   13 fl____t
4 ____ch   14 ____ster
5 k____p   15 scr____m
6 sw____ts   16 scr____n
7 ____gle   17 wh____t
8 qu____n   18 str____t
9 ____ger   19 str____m
10 pl____se   20 cl____n

C Some of the following words contain a long **e** sound, and some do not. Sort out the words into two columns.
Head the columns:

Long e sound	No long e sound

steady, steed, extra, yesterday, yeast, enter, freely, east, bend, hedge, seat, need, neat, head, instead, dread, bee, three

Long Vowel, Silent e

The word **hat** has a short vowel sound.
The word **hate**, because of its final silent **e**,
has a long vowel sound.
When a vowel comes before a consonant
and a final silent **e**, the vowel usually
has a long sound: **rip ripe**

A Fill each blank with one of the words in
brackets. Write the whole sentence.

Question: Jill _____ in the bushes when we
were playing _____-and-seek. (hide, hid)
Answer: Jill hid in the bushes when we were
playing hide-and-seek.

1 The cat followed the _____ at a great
_____ out of the cellar. (rat, rate)

2 My mother said she would _____ write
me a _____ for the teacher. (note, not)

3 The workmen did nothing but _____
around the building _____ all day long.
(site, sit)

4 When the whole family sat down to
_____, the _____ was awful. (dine, din)

5 He asked _____ not to _____ the
shower until it had been repaired. (us, use)

6 The _____ of the _____ clown made the
audience roar with laughter. (fat, fate)

7 The greedy boy sat _____ the table full
of food and _____ the lot. (ate, at)

8 The dog looked _____ after it had had its
coat _____. (cut, cute)

Long i Sound

The long **i** sound is spelled **i** when it is
followed by other sounds in a word: **rider**
Long **i** sound at the end of a word is usually
spelled **y**: **fly**
Long **i** sound is sometimes spelled **ie** at the
end of a word: **die**

B Make words with a long **i** sound by
adding **i**, **y** or **ie**. Write the whole word.

Question: t____dy
Answer: tidy

1 wh____	11 t____ny
2 m____nder	12 ____dle
3 m____	13 t____ger
4 p____	14 l____nesman
5 st____	15 suppl____
6 l____	16 appl____
7 repl____	17 l____brary
8 ____tem	18 rel____
9 unt____	19 b____
10 wh____te	20 ____dentif____

C Here is a sentence containing five long **i**
sounds:
"George told a l<u>ie</u> when he said it was m<u>y</u>
<u>i</u>dea to sl<u>i</u>de on the <u>i</u>ce."
Write a sentence containing four long **i**
sounds. Underline the letters that spell the
long **i** sounds. Do not use the words used in
the example.

Sounds the Same—2

A Fill the blanks in the sentences with the words in brackets. Write the whole sentence. If you are in doubt, look up the meanings of the words in a dictionary.

Question: There will be no _____ until you give your sister a _____ of cake.
(piece, peace)
Answer: There will be no peace until you give your sister a piece of cake.

1 "I _____ you would ruin your _____ clothes with that enormous ice cream."
(new, knew)

2 "You will _____ our necks if you don't use your _____ gently on this icy road!"
(brake, break)

3 Joe _____ the cricket ball high in the air. He watched in horror as it came down _____ the roof of a greenhouse.
(through, threw)

4 In the distance they _____ the approaching sound of a stampeding _____ of bison. (herd, heard)

5 The _____ was tied so loosely that it was _____ difficult for Anne to escape. (not, knot)

6 Mr Marriner bought a new _____ for his yacht at a _____ in a small shop by the harbour. (sale, sail)

7 Jean _____ the first set, and was leading by _____ game to love in the second. (won, one)

8 "_____ you really going to _____ those scruffy jeans to your brother's wedding?"
(wear, were)

Short **u** Sound

B Make words with a short **u** sound by adding **oo**, **u** or **ou**. Write the whole word.

Question: t____k
Answer: took

1 b____k
2 w____d
3 w____ld
4 p____ll
5 h____k
6 h____d
7 sh____ld
8 c____kery
9 cr____k
10 c____ld

11 n____k
12 st____d
13 b____ll
14 f____tball
15 p____sh
16 f____ll
17 childh____d
18 p____dding
19 r____k
20 l____k

C Write six sentences of your own. Use one of these words in each sentence.

1 wear   2 brake   3 through
4 sail   5 won   6 herd

8

Often Misspelled – 2

Some words are often misspelled. When you need to write a word and you are not sure how to spell it, check in your dictionary.

A One word in each sentence is not completed. Each star stands for a missing letter. Complete the word and write the whole sentence.

Question: We arrived at the sta∗∗∗n too late to catch the train.
Answer: We arrived at the station too late to catch the train.

1 Tim's mother gave him a ch∗∗ce between making the beds and washing the dishes.

2 Tim told his mother he would ch∗∗∗e when the film on television had finished.

3 When Tim's mother heard that, she ch∗∗∗ for him. Tim washed the dishes *and* made the beds.

4 When Janet wants to check on the spelling of a word, she looks it up in a di∗∗ion∗ry.

5 I cannot play today, but tom∗∗∗ow will be all right.

6 Even tho∗∗∗ Jane is the smallest girl in the class, she is the fastest runner.

7 The peak of the m∗∗nt∗∗n is covered with snow all the year round.

8 Our dog th∗u∗∗t the cat-flap was for him, too.

Sounds of **ou** and **ow**

The words **pound** and **town** have the same vowel sound. In **pound** the sound is spelled **ou**, and in **town** it is spelled **ow**. The sound is usually spelled **ow** when it comes at the end of a word or syllable, or when it is in a word with a final **n** or **l**.

B Make words by adding **ou** or **ow**. Write the whole word.

1 ____t
2 p____er
3 dr____n
4 pr____d
5 m____th
6 am____nt
7 t____el
8 c____ard
9 ab____t
10 cr____n
11 v____el
12 s____th
13 surr____nd
14 gr____l
15 p____der
16 r____nd
17 c____nty
18 cl____d
19 br____n
20 sh____er

C Find two words that rhyme with each word given.

Example: loud proud cloud

1 shower	2 out	3 crown
4 owl	5 cow	6 pound

Short and Long e Sounds

Two ways of spelling the short **e** sound are **e** and **ea**: f**e**d d**ea**d
(But remember that **ea** is also used to spell the long **e** sound: b**ea**ch)

A Each pair of words has one word containing a short **e** sound, and one word containing a long **e** sound. Say both words to yourself. Then write the word with the short **e** sound.

Question: instead treat
Answer: instead

1 bead, bed
2 ready, reel
3 bread, eat
4 easy, eggs
5 heal, sped
6 heave, heaven
7 weather, tea
8 neat, contest
9 eagle, electric
10 thread, heat

11 meant, meat
12 meal, meadow
13 credit, speak
14 peak, pedal
15 please, pencil
16 steady, steal
17 tether, seat
18 deaf, deal
19 each, eleven
20 wealth, heath

Some Consonant Blends

The vowel letters are **a**, **e**, **i**, **o** and **u**. The other letters are consonants.
Consonants can be blended. That means they are placed together in a word and said very quickly.
These words have consonant blends:
close frost

B Use one of the consonant blends in brackets to complete each unfinished word. Write the whole of each sentence.

1 The ____olar read to the ____udents from a ____oll. (st, sch, scr)

2 When the ____under ____eared away, it became a ____endid afternoon. (spl, th, cl)

3 The ____ength of the ____idge was tested by the ____orm. (br, st, str)

4 Harry won the spri____ in the la____ few metres with a fine bu____ of speed. (nt, rst, st)

5 The waiter ____ipped over the woman's handbag and ____awled on the ____oor amid the ruins of the meal. (spr, fl, tr)

6 The car le____ the rough tra____ and ____unged into the fore____. (ck, st, pl, ft)

7 The clu____ on the car was ____ipping so badly that Jim de____ared it would be quicker to walk. (sl, cl, tch)

8 The ____eeping parrot fell from its pe____ and ____actured its ____ull. (rch, fr, sk, sl)

C Find words that include the following consonant blends. Write one word for each blend. Then write each word in a sentence.

1 pl   2 cr   3 dr   4 tw   5 bl
6 scr   7 str   8 ld   9 spr   10 spl

Sounds of **au** and **aw**

The words **cause** and **straw** have the same vowel sound. In **cause** the sound is spelled **au**, and in **straw** it is spelled **aw**.
The sound is usually spelled **au** when it is followed by one or more other sounds in a word. When the sound comes at the end of a word, it is usually spelled **aw**.
The **aw** spelling is sometimes used in other parts of a word.

A Make words by adding *au* or *aw*. Write the whole word.

1 dr____n
2 p____
3 s____cer
4 y____n
5 f____lt
6 bec____se
7 c____ght
8 s____
9 dr____
10 h____nt

11 astron____t
12 ____tograph
13 ____ful
14 cr____l
15 ____tomatic
16 ____thor
17 d____n
18 j____
19 appl____se
20 ____kward

Sounds the Same – 3

There are some words that sound alike, but have different meanings. They are usually spelled differently – **herd** and **heard** sound the same.

B Fill the blanks in the sentences with the words in brackets. Write the whole sentences. If you are in doubt, check the meanings of the words in a dictionary.

1 The doctor said that Andy's _____ would _____ quite quickly. (heel, heal)

2 You would never think that a bit of a toothache would make a _____ man _____ so loudly. (groan, grown)

3 Vicki was wearing a _____ of ear-rings each shaped like a _____. (pear, pair)

4 I asked the carpenter if he _____ make me a table with the _____ I had brought. (would, wood)

5 Owen was in a great deal of _____ when the _____ of glass cut into his wrist. (pane, pain)

6 The robbers were unable to _____ the jewels from the strong _____ safe. (steel, steal)

7 _____ broken glasses have been repaired, and are ready for collection when _____ ready. (you're your)

8 Elizabeth decided that the best _____ to put her mind at ease was to _____ herself each day. (weigh, way)

C Here are just some of the words that can be made using the letters in the word LIVERPOOL:
I liver pool loop pole rope ill roll plover

See how many words you can make using the letters in WALLUMBILLA (it's a town in Australia).

Give yourself 1 point for a one-letter word, 2 points for a two-letter word, and so on. Try to score 100 points . . . or more.

Plurals

Final Long o Sound

The word **plural** means 'more than one'. Most words are made plural by adding **s**: **horse horses**

When words end in **s**, **x**, **ch**, or **sh**, the plural is made by adding **es**: **bus buses, church churches**

When words end in **f** or **fe**, the plural is usually formed by changing the **f** into **v** and adding **es** or **s**: **shelf shelves, knife knives**

But with some words ending in **f** we simply add **s**: **cliffs chiefs roofs**

A Write the plurals of the following words.

Question: bottle
Answer: bottles

1 aeroplane	11 doctor
2 wife	12 hoof
3 box	13 peach
4 elf	14 package
5 thrush	15 school
6 sausage	16 bush
7 life	17 puff
8 flash	18 business
9 torch	19 toe
10 loaf	20 kiss

There are a number of ways of spelling the final long **o** sound. The most common spelling is **ow**: **low yellow**

In a few words, the final long **o** sound is spelled **oe**: **toe foe**

And in a few other words, the final long **o** sound is spelled **o**: **no so**

B Make words ending with a long **o** sound by adding **ow**, **oe** or **o**. Write the whole word.

1 bl____	11 gr____
2 g____	12 potat____
3 f____	13 hell____
4 elb____	14 sparr____
5 foll____	15 bell____
6 gl____	16 bel____
7 ech____	17 zer____
8 sn____	18 d____
9 wid____	19 pian____
10 w____	20 fell____

C Rewrite the sentences, changing the words in dark type into plurals. You will need to change other parts of the sentences as well.

1 The **bird** was fast asleep on its **perch**.
2 The Indian **chief** raised his hand in greeting.
3 The **princess** arrived for the banquet in a splendid **coach**.

Silent Letters **b**, **g**, **h** and **k**

Some words contain letters that are not sounded, so we call them silent letters.

b is often silent after **m**, and sometimes after other letters: **climb doubt**

g is sometimes silent before **n**: **sign**

h is sometimes silent before a vowel: **hour**

k at the beginning of words is silent before **n**: **knew**

A Silent letters are missing in some of the words in the sentences. Add the silent letters and write the sentences.

Question: After the clim__ he __new that all his lim__s would be stiff in the morning.
Answer: After the climb he knew that all his limbs would be stiff in the morning.

1 The children were dum__ with terror when they heard a __nocking just on the stroke of midnight. They were sure it was the g__ost.

2 Annette soon learned the __nack of feeding the young lam__ that had lost its mother.

3 The plum__er said in a __nowing way that the overall desi__n of the heating system was hopeless.

4 Alan's mother asked him if he would com__ his hair in __onour of his birthday.

5 I tied my handkerchief with a tight __not round the g__astly wound on his __nuckles.

6 There is no dou__t that a __nat is an insect and a __nu is a mammal.

Sounds of **oy** and **oi**

The words **joy** and **coin** have the same vowel sound. In **joy** the sound is spelled **oy**, and in **coin** it is spelled **oi**.
When the sound comes at the end of a word or syllable, it is usually spelled **oy**: **destroy**
When the sound is inside a word, and not at the end of a syllable, it is spelled **oi**: **coil**

B Make words by adding **oy** or **oi**. Write the words.

1 t____
2 r____al
3 b____l
4 av____d
5 enj____
6 cowb____
7 j____ful
8 j____nt
9 sp____l
10 n____se
11 v____age
12 j____n
13 p____nt
14 ann____
15 b____
16 s____l
17 ch____ce
18 destr____
19 t____let
20 rej____ce

C Write six sentences using one of the following in each:

1 A word with a silent **g**
2 A word ending in **oy**
3 A word with a silent **k**
4 A word spelled with **oi**
5 A word with a silent **h**
6 A word with a silent **b**

The good news is that the zoo has two new gnus

13

The k Sound

These words contain the **k** sound:
cat kid took pack

The spelling of the **k** sound is often **c**, but before **e** or **i** it is spelled **k**: **keep kill**

At the end of a word the **k** sound is usually spelled **k** or **ck**: **look cock**

Final **k** sound after two vowels is spelled **k**: **seek**

Final **k** sound after one vowel is spelled **ck**: **check**

A Make a table with four columns, like this:

The k sound		Final k sound	
spelled c	spelled k before e or i	spelled k after 2 vowels	spelled ck after 1 vowel

Make words with the k sound by adding c, k or ck. Write each word in the correct column.

se__ond	pi__	s__ill	tri__
__ing	soa__	clo__	cloa__
__ave	s__our	smo__e	wa__en
coo__ery	sti__	bro__en	ba__on
spea__	pa__age	se__ure	shrie__

Often Misspelled—3

B One word in each sentence is not complete. Each star stands for a missing letter. Complete the word and write the whole sentence.

Question: When in doubt, look in your
di**ion*ry.
Answer: When in doubt, look in your dictionary.

1 The second month of the year is Feb***ry.

2 The day before Thursday is We*e*day.

3 The doctor told the pa***nt that he would have to give up smoking or suffer the consequences.

4 Is it really ne***sary to make that noise when you are drinking your soup?

5 Pam and Sam had a qu***el about whose turn it was to walk the dog.

6 The police ca***t the crook after a long car chase on the motorway.

7 Sparks from the burning wood in the grate set the chi***y on fire.

8 When Dad saw the ele*tri*ity bill, his hair stood on end.

Ele*tri* shock!

C See how many words you can make using the letters in KEINHINGHSIEN (it's a place in China).

Begin with these: skin, hen, neigh.

Give yourself 1 point for a one-letter word, 2 points for a two-letter word, and so on. Try to score 100 points . . . or more.

Sounds of **th**, **wh**, **ch** and **sh**

Some single sounds are spelled by two letters:
th as in **that**
wh as in **what**
ch as in **chin**
sh as in **shop**

A Some of the words in the sentences are incomplete. Complete the words by adding **th**, **wh**, **ch** or **sh**. Write the whole sentence.

Question: _____o told you to have a _____eap lun_____ in this café?
Answer: Who told you to have a cheap lunch in this café?

1 _____is _____eel _____ould be all right for my car.

2 It is selfi_____ to eat too mu_____ food _____en there is su_____ a great deal of hunger in the world.

3 Mo_____er wi_____es _____e had more ca_____ for her weekly _____opping.

4 _____arlie was _____ocked to find _____at the _____air he was going to sit on wasn't _____ere.

5 My grandfa_____er says he is astoni_____ed at the _____eek of _____ildren _____ese days.

6 _____en William tries to _____istle, no_____ing comes out except a ru_____ of hot air.

7 _____o is doing all _____at pu_____ing and _____oving at the back of the queue?

8 The dog _____ow finally fini_____ed _____en yet ano_____er heavy _____ower of rain soaked the animals and _____eir owners.

Words with **ie** and **ei**

In most words, **i** comes before **e**:
die   thief
But after **c**, the **e** comes first: **receive**

Use **i** before **e**
Except after **c**,
And in words with long **a**
Such as **neighbour** and **weigh**.

Some words with **ei** do not follow this rule:
foreign, weird, either, neither, height
When in doubt, check in your dictionary.

B Make words by adding **ie** or **ei**. Write the whole word.

Question: p_____ce
Answer: piece

1 c_____ling	11 n_____ce
2 fr_____nd	12 f_____ld
3 for_____gn	13 r_____gn
4 bel_____ve	14 w_____rd
5 r_____ns	15 rel_____ve
6 l_____	16 sh_____ld
7 p_____	17 v_____n
8 dec_____ve	18 _____ther
9 _____ght	19 rev_____w
10 n_____ther	20 ch_____f

C Write six sentences. Use one of the following words in each of the sentences.

1 weird   2 veil   3 height
4 neighbour 5 deceive   6 foreign

Suffixes

A suffix is an ending that is added to a word to make a new word:
play player playing

The spelling of some words changes when a suffix is added. With one-syllable words ending in a consonant after a vowel, we double the final consonant before adding a suffix that begins with a vowel:
run running skip skipping

With words ending in silent **e**, we drop the **e** before adding a suffix which begins with a vowel: **move moving**

If the suffix begins with a consonant, we keep the **e**: **move movement**

When adding a suffix, never allow two **es** to come together. Drop one of them.

A Make two new words by adding the suffixes in brackets. Write the two new words.

Question: use (ing, ful)
Answer: using, useful

1 work (er, ing)
2 slim (ing, er)
3 care (less, ing)
4 help (ing, er)
5 stop (ed, er)
6 shut (er, ing)
7 bad (ness, ly)
8 fit (est, er)
9 safe (est, ly)
10 direct (ion, ly)
11 content (ment, ed)
12 fault (less, y)
13 hope (ing, less)
14 loud (ly, est)
15 loyal (ty, ist)
16 take (en, ing)
17 plan (ed, er)
18 sick (ness, ly)
19 scarce (est, ly)
20 live (ing, ed)

Sounds the Same—4

There are some words that sound alike, but have different meanings. They are usually spelled differently—**pair** and **pear** sound the same.

B Fill the blanks in each sentence with the words in brackets. Write the whole sentence. If you are in doubt, look up the meanings of the words in a dictionary.

1 When the winger got the _____, the striker began to _____ for a pass. (bawl, ball)

2 When they arrived at _____ destination, no one was _____ to welcome them. (their, there)

3 About a hundred metres from the _____ stood a large _____ tree. (beech, beach)

4 _____ going to be sorry when _____ holiday is over. (their, they're)

5 The draught from the open door _____ out the _____ flame on the gas cooker. (blue, blew)

6 _____ never going to get _____ on time if they don't hurry. (they're, there)

7 Last time Wally used his power drill, he drilled straight through a piece of _____ and then _____ a hole in a water main. (bored, board)

8 The priest decided to _____ the position of the candles on the _____. (alter, altar)

C Write six sentences. Use one of the following words in each sentence:

1 their   2 beach   3 bored
4 altar   5 there   6 blue

Double Consonants

In some words double consonants are used to spell a single consonant sound:
still   battle

In one-syllable words the final consonants **f, l, s** and **z** are usually doubled when they come after one vowel: **roll**

In words of more than one syllable, a double consonant usually shows that the vowel in front stands for a short vowel sound: **muddle**

A Make words by adding a single or a double consonant. Write the whole word.

Question: pe____y n,nn
Answer: penny

1 fi____ l,ll
2 le____on s,ss
3 la____el b,bb
4 bu____ z,zz
5 bo____om t,tt
6 bi____on s,ss
7 bee____ f,ff
8 rea____ l,ll
9 cli____ f,ff
10 sma____ l,ll
11 mi____le d,dd
12 do____ t,tt
13 ma____ s,ss
14 boi____ l,ll
15 sta____ium d,dd
16 sti____ f,ff
17 we____ l,ll
18 ha____y p,pp
19 bu____le b,bb
20 li____ p,pp

Silent Letters
l, t, u and w

Some words contain letters that are not sounded, and so we call them silent letters.
l is often silent before **d, k, m** or **v: calm**
t is often silent when it comes between an **s** sound and an **n** or **l** sound: **listen**
u is sometimes silent before another vowel: **guard**
w is often silent at the beginning of a word before **r** or **ho: who**

B Silent letters are missing in some of the words in the sentences. Add the silent letters and write the whole sentence.

1 They were stopped by the g__ard in front of the cas__le.

2 Daniel __rapped a handkerchief round his injured __rist.

3 When Helen __riggled her tong__e round her mouth, she cou__d feel the cavity in her tooth.

4 The teacher said she wou__d like to ta__k to Ben's father.

5 Lis__en carefully and you will hear someone whis__ling in the wood.

6 In the ca__m after the storm, they searched the __reck for survivors.

7 Malco__m spent all winter b__ilding a boat in the garden shed, and now he can't get it out.

8 The __hole garden glis__ened with frost.

C Make a list of as many words as you can think of which have silent letters in them. Do not include the words used in section B of this exercise or in the silent letter exercise on page 13.

The s Sound

The **s** sound is usually spelled **s**, but sometimes it is spelled **c**. The **s** sound is often spelled **c** before letters **e**, **i** or **y**: **face   circle   bicycle**

Before any letter except **e**, **i** or **y**, the **s** sound is spelled **s**: **last   same**

A number of words do not obey these rules: **trousers   beside   syrup   system   absent   sign**

When in doubt, check in your dictionary.

A Make words with the **s** sound by adding **s** or **c**. Write the whole word.

Question: __lip
Answer: slip

1 __ort
2 __auce
3 __inema
4 mou__e
5 la__e
6 __ity
7 fan__y
8 __ider
9 __ircus
10 __ight

11 ex__ited
12 __car
13 redu__e
14 produ__e
15 __tay
16 __low
17 __ympathy
18 __ymbals
19 for__e
20 __yclone

Mum, I can't find my other trouser

More Plurals

The word **plural** means 'more than one'.

To make the plurals of words ending in **y** after a vowel, add **s**: **key   keys**

For words ending in **y** after a consonant, change the **y** to **i** and add **es**: body   bodies

In words that end in **o** after another vowel, usually add **s**: **radio   radios**

For words that end in **o** after a consonant, usually add **es**: **tomato   tomatoes**

But most words to do with music form their plurals by adding just **s**: **piano   pianos**

B Form the plurals of the following words.

Question: baby
Answer: babies

1 story
2 toy
3 cherry
4 library
5 echo
6 studio
7 banjo
8 berry
9 army
10 holiday

11 hero
12 solo
13 lorry
14 donkey
15 rodeo
16 supply
17 monkey
18 quay
19 potato
20 fly

C1 Some words are the same in the plural and the singular: **sheep   sheep**

2 Some words have a plural form only: **pyjamas**

3 Some words have plurals that are formed in different ways: **tooth   teeth**

Make three lists of words that behave as in 1, 2 and 3.

Long Sound of Two Vowels

In some words two vowels come together. Often the first vowel makes a long sound, while the second is silent:
rain each tie road true

A Make words with the long vowel sound asked for. Add the other vowel that is needed and write the whole word.

Question: w____t   a
Answer: wait

1 cl__n   e
2 s__p   o
3 p__   i
4 s__l   o
5 s__t   e
6 l__st   e
7 w__t   a
8 aven__   u
9 fl__t   o
10 tr__n   a

11 d__   i
12 c__t   o
13 val__   u
14 t__cher e
15 c__st   o
16 __sily   e
17 pl__n   a
18 l__   i
19 resc__   u
20 r__ch   e

Often Misspelled – 4

B One word in each sentence is not complete. Each star stands for a missing letter. Complete the word and write the whole sentence.

Question: Some words are often mis∗∗ell∗d.
Answer: Some words are often misspelled.

1 Soon after leaving school, the girl started her own bus∗∗∗ss.

2 It is dangerous to allow a young child near a para∗∗∗n heater.

3 Because the fish were always fighting, they had to be sep∗r∗ted into different tanks.

4 The Moon is a sat∗∗ite of Earth.

5 The ap∗l∗∗se from the audience was loud and long.

6 Stephen uses most of his l∗∗s∗re playing sports of many different kinds.

7 "Please tell me tr∗∗y what you think of my new hair-style."

8 "Quite sin∗e∗∗ly, it's very nice, but there is a lot of it."

C How many words of three or more letters can you find hidden inside the row of letters? Pick out the words. One is done for you.

ROLSCIENCENPIDOESTADAPWRITERNGRO(HIT)TAIN

19

Final l Sound

The final **l** sound is usually spelled **le**: **bottle**

After **n** or **v**, final **l** is spelled **el**: **channel**

It is also spelled **el** in a few other words: **label**

When in doubt, check in your dictionary.

A Make words with the final l sound by adding le or el. Write the whole word.

Question: batt_____
Answer: battle

1 gent_____
2 twink_____
3 trav_____
4 peop_____
5 ank_____
6 shov_____
7 trow_____
8 cripp_____
9 litt_____
10 tab_____
11 tunn_____
12 grav_____
13 pick_____
14 purp_____
15 coup_____
16 bund_____
17 lev_____
18 troub_____
19 temp_____
20 pudd_____

Sounds the Same—5

There are some words that sound alike but have different meanings. They are usually spelled differently—**toe** and **tow** sound alike.

B Fill the blanks in each sentence with the words in brackets. Write the whole sentence. If you are in doubt, look up the meanings of the words in a dictionary.

1 Brenda had been warned but she still _____ the pony across the busy _____. (rode, road)

2 Although they had _____ the play many times, the last _____ still made them roar with laughter. (seen, scene)

3 When Dad got lost in his car, he said, "The _____ of the trouble is that I didn't work out the _____ properly." (root, route)

4 Tom said he had _____ the book with the _____ cover. (read, red)

5 At breakfast, Karen said it would be a good idea to have a _____ story on the back of the _____ packet. (cereal, serial)

6 Mother _____ me to the chemist for a bottle of _____. (scent, sent)

7 There were _____ of other bushes, but only one _____ bush in the whole garden. (rose, rows)

8 Mrs Smith told her husband that if he would _____ on his own buttons, she would _____ the seeds in the garden. (sow, sew)

C Write six sentences, using one of these words in each:

1 toe   2 tow   3 beet
4 beat   5 bury   6 berry

Short **i** Sound

A Make words with a short **i** sound by adding **i** or **y**. If you are in doubt, check in your dictionary.

Question: s__lly
Answer: silly

1 s__x
2 t__ckle
3 m__th
4 r__ch
5 l__nch
6 m__ssile
7 l__t
8 s__stem
9 m__stery
10 fool__sh
11 p__llow
12 d__nner
13 s__mphony
14 h__mn
15 m__lkman
16 s__llable
17 r__pple
18 pr__nce
19 h__pnotise
20 pr__son

dge, **tch** and **ch**

B Some of the words in the sentences are incomplete. Complete the words by adding **dge**, **tch** or **ch**. Write the whole sentence.

1 My ri____ Auntie Flo has a great deal of knowle____ about the history of the local chur____.

2 Our dog seems to be one big i____. It spends most of the day scra____ing itself.

3 The runaway bus lur____ed on its side, and plunged off the bri____ into the river.

4 The waiter took the porri____ away, and went to fe____ the bacon and eggs.

5 Bill had to have six sti____es in his leg after the rugby match.

6 The ju____ was told that the accused had twenty-four wa____es on each arm when he was searched by the customs officer.

7 Dad is no electrician. When our lo____r tried to swi____ on the light in his bedroom, the washing ma____ine in the ki____en rumbled into action.

8 The wi____'s broom let her down, and she crashed on the top of a hedge.

C Arrange the letters to make words with a short **i** sound:

1 etyssm   2 slilt   3 ikewct
4 yhmt   5 srik   6 tsihryo

Long **u** Sound

The spellings **ue**, **oo** and **o** can all make the long **u** sound: **glue shoot remove**

A Make words with the long **u** sound by adding **ue**, **oo** or **o**. Write the whole word.

1 bl____
2 r____t
3 val____
4 r____m
5 cl____
6 shamp____
7 ball____n
8 m____ving
9 contin____
10 stat____

11 t____l
12 n____se
13 igl____
14 f____l
15 pr____ve
16 resc____
17 gl____m
18 m____n
19 wh____
20 br____m

or, **ore**, **our** and **oar**

The vowel sound followed by **r** in **or** is spelled in different ways in different words:
or in **born** **ore** in **sore** **our** in **pour** **oar** in **roar**

B Make words that contain the vowel sound followed by **r**, as in **or**, by adding **or**, **ore**, **our** or **oar** to the incomplete words. Write the whole sentence.

1 We b____ded our train on platf____m f____.

2 Jan f____ced open the chest, and inside was a h____d of gold.

3 With a r____ of anger, the tennis player left the c____t. The sc____ was f____ty-love.

4 When the act____ tripped over the carpet, the b____d audience clapped and called for an enc____.

5 All Carole's lab____ was wasted when her sav____y pie came out of the oven burnt to a cinder.

6 Please do me a fav____ and move your seat f____ward to its n____mal position.

7 The waving c____n was a gl____ious sight.

8 Mavis t____ open her Christmas parcel, eager to expl____ the contents.

C Write a list of twenty words which contain the spellings **or**, **ore**, **our** and **oar**, and which make the sound **or** as in **tore**. Do not include any of the words used in the exercise in section B. Put some of each spelling in your list.

Often Misspelled–5

A One word in each sentence is not complete. Each star stands for a missing letter. Complete the word and write the whole sentence.

> Question: Medical s∗∗∗nce has helped to make our lives longer.
> Answer: Medical science has helped to make our lives longer.

1 Walter pulled the bung from the bar∗∗∗, and the beer gushed all over the floor.

2 The battle ended in a terrible mas∗ac∗∗ of almost 10 000 men.

3 Linda d∗∗∗ not know the first thing about spelling.

4 "I see you have drawn a new sort of tr∗∗n∗le with four sides!" said the teacher in the voice that Ted dreaded so much.

5 "Get in the qu∗u∗ for your pay in alphabetical order!" roared the sergeant-major at Private Zilman.

6 The boxer was not cons∗∗∗us for long after the beginning of the first round.

7 Mary loves sport and is very keen on ∗∗ysic∗l education.

8 Dad parked the car on a double yellow line op∗∗s∗te the police station.

Final e

> When words end in silent **e**, the **e** is dropped when an ending that begins with a vowel is added: **bake + ing = baking**
>
> Some words end in a long **e** sound spelled **ee**: **free**
>
> When an ending that starts with an **a** or an **i** is added, the final **e** is not dropped: **free + ing = freeing**
>
> But when the ending starts with an **e**, then one **e** is dropped: **free + ed = freed**
> This is so that three **es** are not left together.

B Make new words with the given endings. Write the whole word.

> Question: take + ing
> Answer: taking

1 move + ing	11 see + ing
2 jump + er	12 strike + er
3 love + ly	13 force + fully
4 agree + ed	14 love + liness
5 use + able	15 glee + ful
6 content + edly	16 agree + able
7 race + er	17 flee + ing
8 dive + ed	18 live + ly
9 disagree + ment	19 skate + ing
10 behave + ing	20 truth + fully

C Write one word with each of these endings: **ing, er, ed, ly, able, edly, ment, ful, fully, ous, ious**. Do not use any of the words from section B.

ear, ere, eer, er, ier

The vowel sound followed by **r** as in the word **ear**, is spelled in different ways in different words: **ear** in **dear**   **ere** in **here**
eer in **cheer**   **er** in **serial**   **ier** in **fierce**

A Some of the words in the sentences are not complete. Complete the words by adding ear, ere, eer, er or ier, so that each word contains the vowel sound followed by r, as in the word ear.

1 The motor engin____ said that the g____s on the car would have to be repaired.

2 The brave hero caught the sp____ and hurled it back f____cely at his enemy.

3 The author was unable to finish the s____ial story when his b____d got caught up in his typewriter.

4 When Dad tried to interf____ with Mum's cooking, she told him to take a long walk down a short p____.

5 This television s____ies is about the s____ious problems of helping the millions of people in the world who are hungry.

6 Philip had a sev____ wound where the sword had p____ced his chest.

7 Grandad always switches off his h____ing-aid when we eat our c____eal for breakfast.

8 The crowd at the rodeo began to ch____ as the cowboy tried to ride the bucking st____.

Changing y to i

When most endings are added to a word ending in a consonant plus **y**, then the **y** is changed to **i**: **study** + **ed** = **studied**

When a word ends in a vowel plus **y**, then the **y** is not changed: **play** + **ed** = **played**

A word ending in a consonant plus **y** does not have the **y** changed when the ending added begins with **i**:
study + **ing** = **studying**

B Spell new words by adding the ending. Write the whole word.

Question: try + ed
Answer: tried

1 copy + ed
2 easy + est
3 boy + ish
4 worry + er
5 dirty + ness
6 annoy + ance
7 country + es
8 destroy + ed
9 marry + ing
10 happy + ness
11 play + ful
12 stray + ed
13 slippery + ness
14 heavy + er
15 cry + ing
16 lady + es
17 sway + ing
18 berry + es
19 pretty + est
20 stay + ed

C See how many words you can make using the letters in
YSTRADGYNLAIS (it's a place in Wales)

Begin with these: strand, digs, glass.

Give yourself 1 point for a one-letter word, 2 points for a two-letter word, and so on. Try to score 100 points . . . or more.

Sounds the Same – 6

There are some words that sound alike but have different meanings.
They are usually spelled differently—
cereal and **serial** sound alike.

A Fill the blanks in each sentence with the words in brackets. Write the whole sentence. If you are in doubt, look up the meanings of the words in a dictionary.

1 High over the broad _____ they could see a _____ circling. (plane, plain)

2 Jack went _____ when he saw the _____ hurtling down the hill towards him. (pale, pail)

3 They stopped outside a fishmonger's shop. David said, "This is the _____ where I bought that large _____ for dinner." (plaice, place)

4 The wounded soldier tried to _____ his eyes to look on the last _____ of the setting sun. (rays, raise)

5 The rocket _____ like a thrusting _____ into a bank of dark cloud. (sword, soared)

6 Using his _____, our dog _____ just where to find sweets in our house. (knows, nose)

7 Watching my Dad sorting out a _____ of tangled fishing line is a _____ treat. (reel, real)

8 Old Fred was just about to _____ an orange when a _____ of bells from the church announced time for the evening service. (peel, peal)

Soft c and g

When a single letter **c** is followed by **e, i** or **y**, the **c** stands for an **s** sound: **city**

When a single letter **g** is followed by **e, i** or **y**, the **g** sometimes stands for a **j** sound: **giant**

B Make words by adding letter **c, s, g** or **j**. Write the whole word.

1 __ity
2 be__ide
3 __ypsy
4 re__pect
5 __entle
6 spa__e
7 re__ect
8 __ilver
9 pen__il
10 __acket
11 an__el
12 sta__e
13 de__ide
14 __eagull
15 bi__ycle
16 __ourney
17 wa__es
18 __and
19 re__oice
20 sin__ere

C Make a list of six words containing each of the following sounds:

1 soft **c** making the **s** sound, as in **space**.
2 hard **c** making the **k** sound, as in **careful**.
3 soft **g** making the **j** sound, as in **general**.
4 hard **g** as in **gun**.

Spellings **qu** and **cu**

The letter **q** in English is always followed by the letter **u**. **qu** stands for a **kw** sound:
queen
The letters **cu** are sometimes confused with **qu**.
In some words **cu** sometimes stands for a **kyu** sound: **cute**
In other words **cu** can have different sounds, as in **curse**.

A Complete the incomplete words in the sentences by adding **qu** or **cu**. Write the whole of each sentence.

1 The ____rate give a ____ick sermon, but it was very much to the point.

2 The audience in the theatre went ____iet as the ____rtain went up.

3 The ____estion is, how are we going to play snooker now that you've broken our only ____e?

4 The boy had to be res____ed by the fire brigade when he fell into the ____arry.

5 The drink they gave us to ____ench our thirst had a most pe____liar taste.

6 The four sides of a s____are all e____al.

7 The detective said that a ____rious se____ence of events had led up to the murder.

8 The man ____ivered all over when the doctor told him that the only ____re was hard physical exercise.

are, air, ear

The sound **are** in **care** is often made with other spellings:
air in **hair**   **ear** in **wear**

B Read the clues. Then complete the words by adding **are**, **air** or **ear**. Write out the whole word.

1 Sit on it   ch____
2 To look hard   st____
3 An animal   b____
4 Clothing next to your skin   underw____
5 Frightened   sc____d
6 A female horse   m____
7 Wild animal's resting-place   l____
8 To shine with a dazzling
   light   gl____
9 Left over   sp____
10 We breathe this   ____
11 A trap   sn____
12 To use bad language   sw____
13 To pull apart   t____
14 Light-coloured   f____
15 Only just   b____ly

C Write a list of words containing **ear** that do not contain the sound **ear** as in **wear**.

26

Often Misspelled—6

A One word in each sentence is not complete. Each star stands for a missing letter. Complete the word and write the whole sentence.

> Question: Many birds fr***e to death in severe winters.
>
> Answer: Many birds freeze to death in severe winters.

1 My mother says I always emba**as* her when we have guests at home.

2 When they lifted the mat**es* off the bed, they found the stolen documents underneath.

3 The letter **e** o**urs in print more often than any other letter.

4 My grandfather says the Gover***nt should provide free food for senior citizens.

5 The street in which we live runs paral**l to the railway line.

6 As Clare passed the cem*t**y, she thought she saw a white shape moving round the headstones.

Doubling the Final Consonant

> When an ending is added to a one-syllable word which ends with one vowel plus one consonant, then the consonant is doubled:
> **bat + ing = batting**
>
> In other words the consonant is not doubled: **find + ing = finding**

B Complete each word by adding the ending. Write the whole word.

1 stop + ed	11 ask + ed
2 big + est	12 step + ing
3 bring + ing	13 ring + ing
4 child + ren	14 sprint + er
5 look + ed	15 wed + ing
6 swim + er	16 strain + ed
7 run + ing	17 shut + er
8 stand + ing	18 proud + est
9 wrap + ed	19 hot + est
10 sad + est	20 slam + ed

C Write six sentences of your own, using one of the answer words from section **A** in each sentence.

7 My sister wants to be a hairdresser. Every time she picks up a pair of s***sors, I run to my bedroom and lock the door.

8 My father borrows books from the lib***y every Saturday.

Sounds the Same – 7

ng and nk

There are some words that sound alike, but have different meanings.
They are usually spelled differently – **pray** and **prey** sound alike.

The spelling **ng** makes the end sound in the word **wing**.

The spelling **nk** makes the end sound in the word **wink**.

A Fill the blanks in each sentence with the words in brackets. Write the whole sentence. If you are in doubt, look up the meanings of the words in a dictionary.

1 My sister started on her third cream cake, and said, "Here goes! It's a _____ of time trying to keep my _____ down." (waist, waste)

2 The rain began to _____ down as the captain led his _____ on to the field. (team, teem)

3 The villain _____ the heroine's wrists and ankles together, and left her on the beach as the _____ was coming in. (tied, tide)

4 The old woman told us an unlikely _____ about a huge dog she had owned that knocked out a burglar with one blow of its _____. (tale, tail)

5 A bomb was _____ at the king as he sat on his _____. (throne, thrown)

6 Father and _____ stood by the lake and watched the _____ setting behind the distant hills. (son, sun)

7 We arrived late for church. Harold said, "I _____ you the bell ____ ages ago." (tolled, told)

8 To our amazement the old man placed one hand on the _____ and vaulted over in fine _____. (style, stile)

B Complete the words by adding ng or nk. Write the whole word.

1 tha____s
2 so____
3 le____th
4 ru____
5 dri____
6 bla____
7 bri____ing
8 bli____ing
9 stro____est
10 astoundi____
11 thro____
12 alo____side
13 stri____
14 stre____th
15 thi____ing
16 spa____
17 shri____ing
18 fli____ing
19 confusi____
20 fla____

C How many words of four or more letters can you find hidden inside the row of letters? Pick out the words. One is done for you.

FONB(CRANK)RESNKAHANGINGHOSKRA-
NGERKONANKLEFROSB

YIPPEE!

ex and exc

ex and exc come at the beginning of many words, and they can be confused:
exact   except

A Make words by adding **ex** or **exc**. Write the whole word.

1 ____use
2 ____ess
3 ____ert
4 ____tra
5 ____ite
6 ____ercise
7 ____plode
8 ____claim
9 ____hange
10 ____pert

11 ____ellent
12 ____ist
13 ____pand
14 ____ursion
15 ____pel
16 ____press
17 ____eption
18 ____hibition
19 ____perience
20 ____lamation

Unusual Long Vowels

Long vowel sounds are sometimes spelled in unusual ways.
In this word the long **a** sound is spelled **ea**:
break
In this word the long **e** sound is spelled **i**:
police
In this word the long **i** sound is spelled **igh**:
might
In these words the long **o** sound is spelled **ou** and **oa**: **soul   loaf**
In these words the long **u** sound is spelled **ou** and **ui**: **youth   juice**

B Complete the incomplete words in the sentences by adding unusual long vowels. Write the whole sentences.

1 The food on the Mediterranean cr____se was excellent.

2 Dinner began with a wide choice of s____ps.

3 Then I usually had a st____k or some p____ltry.

4 One evening I had some very tasty r____st sh____lder of lamb.

5 There was plenty of fresh fr____t.

6 At midday it was so hot that I usually had a l____t lunch.

7 There were fruit j____ces of all kinds, and the sard____nes were delicious.

8 All the people in our gr____p enjoyed themselves, so it is possible that we m____t go again next year.

C Write six sentences of your own, using one of the following words in each sentence:

1 expand   2 exclamation 3 exert
4 exclaim   5 excess   6 exception

Often Misspelled – 7

A One word in each sentence is not complete. Each star stands for a missing letter. Complete the word and write the whole sentence.

Question: Our dog is fri**tened of thunder.
Answer: Our dog is frightened of thunder.

1 The chairman's sp**ch lasted for an hour, and we all thought it was sixty minutes too long.

2 Mrs Baker knew from the colour of Katy's tong** who had stolen the blackcurrant tart.

3 Margaret knows some French, but her pron*n*i*tion is not very good.

4 Miners have to de**end into the depths of the earth to do their dirty and dangerous work.

5 One of the actors got so annoyed with the **dience that he refused to go on with the play.

6 The inventor is trying to make a cheaper f**l than petrol for motor cars.

7 Mother's eyes always fill with tears when she de**ribes how Father proposed to her.

8 Uncle Norman says he once ta***t his dog to switch off the alarm clock every morning.

More of the **aw** Sound

In some words the **aw** sound is spelled **aw**, as in **straw**.

In other words it is spelled **au**, as in **fault**.

The **aw** sound can also be spelled **augh**, as in **caught**.

And it can be spelled **ough**, as in **bought**.

B Make words with the **aw** sound by adding **aw**, **au**, **augh** or **ough**. Write the whole word.

1 l____n
2 ____tumn
3 sp____n
4 n____ty
5 f____t
6 ____dience
7 n____t
8 d____ter
9 th____t
10 ____e
11 ____t
12 h____ty
13 br____t
14 pr____n
15 sl____ter
16 s____t
17 y____ning
18 s____nter
19 ____kwardness
20 n____tical

C See how many words you can make using the letters in
AUCHTERMUCHTY (it's a place in Scotland)

Begin with these: term, catch, teach, treat.

Give yourself 1 point for a one-letter word, 2 points for a two-letter word, and so on. Try to score 100 points . . . or more.

Sounds the Same – 8

There are some words that sound alike but have different meanings.
They are usually spelled differently –
pause and **paws** sound alike.

A Fill the blanks in each sentence with the words in brackets. Write the whole sentence. If you are in doubt, look up the meanings of the words in a dictionary.

1 It was late at _____ when the _____ at last reached the castle to rescue the fair maiden who was in distress. (night, knight)

2 I don't like the way that large dog _____ at me every time I pass it on the _____. (stairs, stares)

3 Ron decided he needed _____ rest before tackling the next _____. (some, sum)

4 The _____ saved money by giving up his Rolls-Royce and riding about the town on a _____. (mare, mayor)

5 The teacher said, "It will _____ the agony of this spelling _____ if you would all take out your dictionaries." (lesson, lessen)

6 Rather than show the ruined meal to her husband, Thelma buried the _____ dinner in a _____ in the garden. Then she went out and bought a Chinese take-away. (whole, hole)

7 The _____ told his followers that it would be of _____ to their souls to listen to his words of wisdom. (profit, prophet)

8 Please _____ that you have signed your _____ before you put it in the post. (cheque, check)

Hard c and g

Letter **c** can stand for a hard sound, as in **cot**.
Letter **g** can stand for a hard sound, as in **gun**.

B Make words with a hard **c** or **g** sound, or both, by adding c or g, or both, to the following. Write the whole word.

1 re__ord
2 wi__
3 __uitar
4 __uess
5 __ube
6 __or__i
7 __ust
8 be__in
9 __arpet
10 dis__ount
11 __o__
12 __uilty
13 __ollect
14 __o__ __les
15 s__raped
16 __race
17 slo__
18 re__o__nise
19 __lown
20 __own

C Correct the following misspellings:

1 thier
2 iland
3 lazee
4 breake
5 ment
6 wayt
7 climing
8 strau
9 eqwel
10 ekstra
11 stashun
12 schratch
13 packaje
14 Febuary
15 wallpeaper
16 sinsere
17 repli
18 krown
19 astronawt
20 sparroe
21 nesessary

Index